8241 - 8258

Victorian Songs

&

Duets

CHICAGO PUBLIC LIBRARY
R00941 24985

DISCARD

Edited and introduced by
Robert Tear

D1206551

as sung by

Robert Tear & Benjamin Luxon

Cramer

ACKNOWLEDGEMENTS

J.B. Cramer & Co., Ltd., wish to thank those publishers who have granted permission for their works to be used in this volume and also the Performing Rights Society for their help in tracing the copyright owners.

"Tom Bowling", "My Snowy-Breasted Pearl" and "Wee Cooper of Fife"

© Copyright by Bayley and Ferguson Ltd.,
65 Berkeley Street, Glasgow G3 7DX.
Reproduced by permission.

"The Larboard Watch"

© Copyright 1951 by Beal Stuttard & Co., 219 Tottenham Court Road, London W.1.
Reproduced by permission.

"Big Lady Moon"

©Copyright 1909 Boosey and Co.
Reproduced by permission of Boosey and Hawkes Music Publishers Ltd., 295 Regent Street, London W1.

"Watchman! What Of The Night?"

© Copyright 1905 Boosey and Co.
Reproduced by permission of Boosey and Hawkes Music Publishers Ltd., 295 Regent Street, London W1.

"Tenor and Baritone"

© Copyright 1914 by Reeder and Walsh, 138/140 Charing Cross Road, London W.C.2.
Reproduced by permission of EMI Music Publishing Ltd., 138/140 Charing Cross Road, London WC2H 0LD.

"The Children's Home"

© Copyright by Leonard, Gould & Bolttler., 24 Boreham Road, London N22.
Reproduced by permission.

Cover photograph © Copyright by Clive Barda (London)
Reproduced by permission.

Copyright 1980 J. B. Cramer & Co., Ltd., 23 Garrick Street, London WC2E 9AX.

All rights reserved. No part of this publication may be reproduced, stored in a retrieval system or transmitted, in any form or by any means, electronic, mechanical, photocopying, recording or otherwise, without the prior permission of the Copyright owner.

Book design and music setting by Polly Productions

Printed in England by Halstan & Co. Ltd., Amersham, Bucks, England

CONTENTS

Book design & music setting by Polly Productions

INTRODUCTION

MUSIC INFORMATION CENTER
VISUAL & PERFORMING ARTS
CHICAGO PUBLIC LIBRARY

The music of the Victorians has been strangely neglected.   Their poems and
their pictures have received a great deal of serious interest and critical acclaim,
and yet one hears almost no mention of their music.   One does, of course,
hear people giving their rather superior opinions of certain songs like "Come
into the Garden, Maud", but rarely does one hear a serious word spoken.
That this view of Victorian art was rather unbalanced became apparent to me
about ten years ago when I became interested in English painters, including
Victorians like Ford-Maddox Brown, Millais, Rossetti, Ruskin and others.

When I met Ben Luxon on another engagement we both discovered that
our grandparents had adored the songs of the Victorians, and this inspired us
to look closely into the whole oeuvre.   As well as re-discovering some excellent
individual songs we were able to draw some interesting general conclusions.

It soon became clear that Victorian musical style was very closely associated
with the 'bel canto' school of Italian composers; the free and beautiful vocal
lines of Rossini, Donizetti, Bellini and Verdi were clearly mirrored in the
music of Benedict, Brahms and Balfe, but the other aspect of the style - namely
the prevailing, high romantic, gothic nature of Victorian thought was unexpected.
Another characteristic of the period was the idea that no work of art - whether
it be poem, picture or song - was really complete until it not only contained a
strong 'message', but also that this was hammered home.

What we were especially concerned with was this strange piquant, not to
say eccentric, combination of late 18th and early 19th century Italian vocal
freedom with the tighter Germanic, highly romantic thoughts of the most
influential contemporary thinkers.   The consequent and strange hybrid of
this union is a song such as "Annabelle Lee" by Henry Leslie and Edgar Allan
Poe.   The music, which is set to the gently flowing rhythm of a Siciliana, is
beautifully limpid; the text, however, deals with a love affair which has come
to an end with the great rapist's death, and closes with the superbly romantic
picture of the lover lying by the side of his beloved's tomb on the seashore,
under the light of a heavily watchful moon.

Obviously to the more cynical eyes of the last fifty years such romantic
notions and gestures have not been acceptable.   Yet more recently, as we have
moved farther from the actual time, these ideas and ideals have come to be
seen in a clearer light.   Ruined castles, maidens in distress, the presence of
cobwebs in profusion, the idea of love until death - all may be seen as visions
of an eminently exciting yet unreachable world, a world ages apart from the
largely cosy, comfortable and overconfident world which they in truth inhabited.
The Victorians' constant awareness of the horrible poverty amongst them is
shown in some songs in which the rich child, on meeting the poor child, asks
the most insensitive questions and is answered with angelic sweetness and
innocence.   Conscience is thereby stilled for a while.   Such observations,
however interesting socially, are only garnishings covering the most interesting
and exciting songs.   Ben and I have derived tremendous pleasure from performing
them, and have sung them to capacity audiences all over the country.   The
enjoyment of the listeners is written on their faces.   We believe that each
song should be performed with honesty and directness, and never with tongue
in cheek, unless this is obviously appropriate.   The Victorian composers
knew their jobs, and one must trust them in order to receive great satisfaction
in the performing of their works.

The selection of songs has been quite a difficult problem.   With a literature
so wide and far ranging in mood one hardly knows where to begin.   So we
decided on a compromise and have included many of the most popular songs
together with some which in our view have been wrongly neglected.   We hope
you will enjoy performing them.

Robert Tear.

ANNABELLE LEE

Words by EDGAR ALLAN POE

Music by HENRY LESLIE

© Copyright J. B. Cramer & Co. Ltd., 23 Garrick Street, London WC2E 9AX
All rights reserved.

Plate No. 16400

love that the wing-ed se-raphs of Hea-ven co-vet-ed her__ and me.

And this was the rea-son that,

long a - go, In this king-dom by the sea. A

wind blew out of a cloud, chil-ling My beau-ti-ful An - na - belle

all the night-tide I lie down by the side Of my dar - ling, my dar - ling, my

life and my bride, In her se - pul - chre there by the sea___ In her

tomb by the sound - ing sea. My beau - ti - ful An - na - belle

Lee. My beau - ti - ful An - na - belle __ Lee. ___

BIG LADY MOON

Words by KATHLEEN EASMON

Music by S. COLERIDGE—TAYLOR

© Copyright 1909 Boosey and Co.

Reproduced by permission of Boosey & Hawkes Music Publishers Ltd., 295 Regent St.,London W1.

Plate No. 16400

Lyrics:
So you see I'll have to go, I hope you won't be lone - ly though, 'Cos I love you e - ver so, Big La - dy Moon! Big La - dy Moon!

THE CAROL SINGERS

Words by CHARLES HAYES

Music by T.C. STERNDALE—BENNETT

In our vil - lage, Christ - mas time, I sez to sev - 'ral mates, "Look 'ee lads," I

sez, sez I, "Now what a - bout some waits?" We gets a car - ol,___ larns it up, An'___

on an ev - nin' win - try, We muf - fles up an'___ sal - lies forth, To___ try it on the

© Copyright J.B. Cramer & Co. Ltd., 99 St.Martin's Lane, London WC2N 4AZ.
All rights reserved.

Plate No. 16400

gin - try. "Good King Wen - ces - las look'd out," Sings

we with splen - did pow - wer, Sev - 'ral neigh-bours look'd out too, To see what all the

row were! We sings for - te, soun-ded like a hun - derd, Ev - en in the soft bits

'ow we thun - dered! Bill, our bass, 'e 'urt 'is face, (We thought that it were torn!) But

mf a tempo

rall.

mf a tempo

Plate No. 16400

all a - gree there were none like we, To__ 'ail the 'ap - py morn.____

Per - kins took the tre - ble line, A love - ly voice 'e's got;____ I were ten - or,

Bill were bass An' Fred were all the lot, 'E wan - der'd up an'__ down the scale, But__

Plate No. 16400

still 'e ra-ther marred it, Be-cos 'e ne-ver__ know'd no words An'__

so 'e 'la la la'd' it.

"La la la la la look'd out," Sings 'e with splen-did pow - wer, Sev-'ral neigh-bours

look'd out too, To see what all the row were! We sings for-te,

soun-ded| like a hun-derd,| Ev - en in the soft bits 'ow we thun-dered! Ev - 'ry verse got

worse an' worse,| But though we all felt worn, Yet all a - gree there were none like we, To

'ail the 'ap - py morn.

Still we nev - er got no cash, Which did - n't seem quite just,

See-in' we'd stood there fer hours, A' sing-in' fit to bust,____ Then our p'lice-man,

ole Bob Bates, Comes up a' scow-lin' pro-per, "Good old Bob," young

rall.

Per - kins sez, "At___ last we've got a cop-per."

mf a tempo

"Good King Wen-ces - las look'd out," We still keeps on re-cord-in',

THE CHILDREN'S HOME

Words by
F. E. WEATHERLY

F.H. COWEN
Arranged by ALFRED J. CALDICOTT

© Copyright by Leonard, Gould & Bolttler., 24 Boreham Road, London N22.
Reproduced by permission.

Plate No. 16400

Once he had given her a flower, And Oh! how he smiled to see Her

Once he had given her a flower, And Oh! how he smiled to see Her

thin white hands through the rail - ings, Stretched out so ea - ger - ly. She

thin white hands through the rail - ings, Stretched out so ea - ger - ly.

came a - gain to the gar - den, She saw the chil - dren play, But the

She came a - gain, She saw, she saw the chil - dren play, But the

lit-tle white face had van - ished, The lit-tle feet gone a - way.

lit-tle white face had van - ished, The lit-tle feet gone a - way.

Down

She crept a-way to her cor - ner, Down

by the mur-ky stream; But the pale, pale face in the gar - den Shone

by the mur-ky stream; The pale face Shone

COME INTO THE GARDEN, MAUD

Words by ALFRED, LORD TENNYSON

Music by M.W.BALFE

Come in - to the gar - den, Maud, For the black bat, night, has flown; Come in - to the gar - den, Maud, I am here at the gate a-

© Copyright J.B. Cramer & Co. Ltd., 99 St.Martin's Lane, London WC2N 4AZ.
All rights reserved.

Plate No. 16400

-lone, I am here,— at the gate a - lone, And the wood-bine spi - ces are

waft - ed a - broad, And the musk of the ro - ses blown, For a breeze of morn - ing

moves,— And the pla-net of Love is on high; Be - gin - ning to faint in the

light that she loves, On a bed of daf-fo - dil sky, To

faint in the light — of the sun — she loves, — to faint — in his light, — and to die. Come! — Come!

Come in - to the gar - den, Maud, For the black bat, night, has flown,

Come in - to the gar - den, Maud, I am

Gar - den of girls, Come hi - ther, the dances are done, In gloss of sa - tin and glim-mer of pearls, Queen, li - ly, and rose, in one _____. Shine out, lit - tle head, sun-ning o - ver with curls, To the flow - ers and be _____ their sun. Shine out! Shine out! and be their sun.

Plate No. 16400

THE DICKY BIRD AND THE OWL

Words by MARGARET A. SINCLAIR

Music by Sir ARTHUR S. SULLIVAN

©Copyright J.B. Cramer & Co. Ltd., 99 St.Martin's Lane, London WC2N 4AZ.
All rights reserved.

Plate No. 16400

voice so fine, Such beau-ty of tone is a

-dee, Twee-dle- ee - dle - dee, Twee-dle - ee - dle - dee, Twee-dle- ee - dle - dee, Twee-dle- ee - dle -

gift di - vine, I'll sing my notes from

-dee, Twee-dle- ee - dle -dee, Twee-dle- ee - dle - dee, Twee-dle- ee - dle - dee, Twee-dle- ee - dle -

"A" to "G" And an op - -'ra "star" I will

-dee, Twee-dle- ee - dle - dee, Twee-dle- ee - dle - dee, Twee-dle- ee - dle - ee - ee - ee -

"G," an op - e - ra "star" I will some day be.____

- dee, Twee-dle-ee - dle-dee, Twee-dle -ee-dle - dee, he will some day be.____

BARITONE *legato* *mf*

On high in the tree dwelt a bach-el -or owl, A grim old cus-to -mer

simile

he, ("That fel-low," he cried, with fer - o - cious scowl, "Will soon be my death I can

see!" He sings by night, he sings by day, Oh, would that his lease would ex -

- pire next May! For no - thing on earth can be such a bore As

mu-si-cal folk in the house, The house next door, the house next door.

TENOR a tempo

Twee-dle-ee-dle-

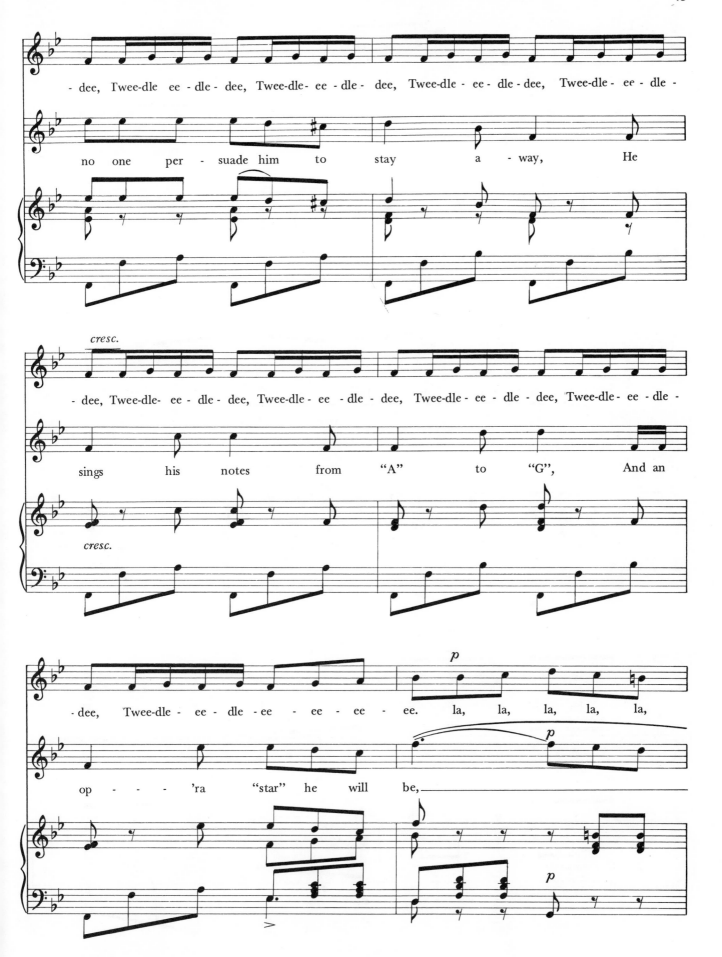

EXCELSIOR!

Words by LONGFELLOW

Music by M. W. BALFE

Moderato

TENOR

The shades of night__ were fal-ling fast, As thro' an Alp-ine vil-lage pass'd__ A youth, who bore 'mid snow and ice A ban - ner, with the strange de-vice, 'Ex - cel - si - or! Ex - cel - si - or!' His brow was sad, his eye be-neath Flash'd like a fal - chion from its

© Copyright J.B. Cramer & Co. Ltd., 99 St.Martin's Lane, London WC2N 4AZ.
All rights reserved.

Plate No. 16400

- on this breast,' A tear stood in his bright blue eye, But still ___ he ans-wered, with a sigh,

cresc.

mp TENOR & BASS

'Ex - cel - si - or! Ex - cel - si - or!' 'Be - ware the

p

BASS

pine ___ trees' with - er'd branch, Be - ware the aw - ful a - va -

- lanche,' This was the pea - sant's last good-night;

There in the twi - light cold _____ and grey,

There in the twi - light cold _____ and grey,

Life - less, but beau - ti - ful _____ he

Life - less, but beau - ti - ful _____ he

lay, And from the sky se - rene _____ and

lay, And from the sky se - rene _____ and

FLOW GENTLY, DEVA

Words and Music by JOHN PARRY

© Copyright J.B. Cramer & Co. Ltd., 99 St.Martin's Lane, London WC2N 4AZ.
All rights reserved.

Plate No. 16400

Then shall the Bards, then shall the Bards, in sad notes, Sad notes

Then shall the Bards, shall the Bards, in sad notes, Sad notes

ring our knell.

Or chant in hap-py strains the

ring our knell

Or chant in hap-py

song, the song of joy, Then shall the Bards in

strains the song, the song of joy, the Bards in

the song of joy, The song of joy,_____ the song of

song of joy, The song of joy,_____ the song of

joy, will_ chant,_____ Will chant,_____ The

joy, The Bards will chant,_____ the Bards will chant,_____ The

Bards, the Bards will chant, chant_the song_ of joy.

Bards, the Bards will chant, chant the song_____ of joy.

GENDARMES' DUET

Words by H. B. FARNIE

Music by OFFENBACH

© Copyright J.B. Cramer & Co. Ltd., 99 St.Martin's Lane, London WC2N 4AZ.
All rights reserved.

Plate No. 16400

there!

Or lit - tle boys that do no

But when we meet a help - less wo - - man,

harm,

We run them in,

we run them in,

We show them

We run them in,

we run them in,

we're the bold Gen - darmes.

We run them in,

We run them in,

we run them

cresc -

we run them in, We show them we're the bold Gen - darmes!

in, we run them in, We show them we're the bold Gen - darmes!

Some-times our du - ty's ex - tra -

Then lit - tle but - ter - flies we chase!

- mur - al,

We like to gam - bol in things

night,   Pro - vi - ded

We're quite dis--pos'd to keep it qui - - et,

that they make it   right!   Or give to

But if they do not seem to   see   it,

us   our pro - per   terms!   We run them in,

We run them in,   we run them

LARBOARD WATCH

Arranged by R.S. THORNTON

by T. WILLIAMS

© Copyright 1951 by Beal Stuttard & Co., 219 Tottenham Court Road, London W.1.
Reproduced by permission.

Plate No. 16400

74

LIST TO THE CONVENT BELLS

by JOHN BLOCKLEY

© Copyright J.B. Cramer & Co. Ltd., 99 St.Martin's Lane, London WC2N 4AZ.
All rights reserved.

Plate No. 16400

O - ver the rip - pling sea; Bright yon moon is beam - ing

O - ver the rip - pling sea; Bright yon moon is beam - ing

cresc.

O - ver each tow'r and tree, The waves seem list - ening to the sound, As si - lent - ly they

O - ver each tow'r and tree, The waves seem list - ening to the sound, As si - lent - ly they

p

flow____ O'er cor - al ___ groves and fair - y ___ ground, And spark - ling caves be-

flow____

sail in our bark (the fleet - est) To a sweet mel - o - dy. Then as we're gent-ly

sail in our bark (the fleet - est) To a sweet mel - o - dy. Then as we're gent-ly

sail - ing, We'll sing that plain-tive strain,_____ which mem-'ry makes en - dear - ing, And

sail - ing, We'll sing that plain-tive strain,_____ which mem-'ry makes en - dear - ing, And

home re - calls a - gain._____ List! 'tis mu - sic steal - ing O - ver the rip - pling

home re - calls a - gain._____ List! 'tis mu - sic steal - ing O - ver the rip - pling

sea; Bright yon moon is beam - ing O - ver each tow'r and tree.

sea; Bright yon moon is beam - ing O - ver each tow'r and tree.

List! list! list to the con-vent bells! List! list!

List! list! list to the con-vent bells! List! list!

list to the con - vent_ bells!

list to the con - vent_bells!

THE MOON HAS RAISED HER LAMP ABOVE

Words by JOHN OXENFORD

Music by Sir JULIUS BENEDICT

moon has rais'd her lamp a-bove, To light the way to thee, my love, to light____ the

way____ to thee____ my love; Her rays up-on the wa-ters play, to

© Copyright J.B. Cramer & Co. Ltd., 99 St.Martin's Lane, London WC2N 4AZ.
All rights reserved.

Plate No. 16400

tell me eyes more bright than they Are watch-ing thro' the night_____ Are watching thro'___ the

night!___ I come,_____ I come,___ my heart's_____ de - light,_____ I come,___ I

come,___ my heart's___ de - light,___ I come,___ I come,___ I come, my heart's de-

-light!   I come, I come, my heart's de-light!

THE SNOWY-BREASTED PEARL

THERE'S A COLLEEN FAIR AS MAY

Translated from the Irish by Dr. PETRIE

Arranged by ALFRED MOFFAT

1. There's a col - leen fair as May, for a year and for a day, I have sought by ev - 'ry way her heart to gain.
There's no___

2. O thou bloom - ing milk - white dove, to whom I've giv'n true love, Do not ev - er thus re - prove my con - stan - cy.
There are___

© Copyright by Bayley and Ferguson Ltd.,
65 Berkeley Street, Glasgow G3 7DX.
Reproduced by permission.

Plate No. 16400

TENOR AND BARITONE

Words by A. BROUGHTON BLACK

Music by H. LANE WILSON

©Copyright 1914 by Reeder and Walsh,
Reproduced by permission of E.M.I. Music Publishing Ltd., 138 - 140 Charing Cross Rd.,London W.C.2

Plate No. 16400

-fec-tive - ly; Song or du - et, Both show our art,

-fec-tive - ly; Song or du - et, Both show our

Tri - o, Quar - tet, each takes his part But O! for the pow'r that the

art, Tri - o, Quar - tet, takes his part Then O! for the pow'r that the

vo - ca -list can sway, And O! for the mu - sic that makes us glad and gay; For a

vo - ca -list can sway, And O! for the mu - sic that makes us glad and gay; For a

sing— to fair dam - sels a - gain— and a - gain, For a Ten - or's in

love at all times._____ His sweet - heart re - joi - ces in

sev - e - ral names_____ Ma - ry, An - na - bel, Sue_____

But it mat - - ters not if he has num - ber - less flames A

voice to call his own, He may ei - ther be a Te-nor, A sweet me - lo-dious Ten - or, Or

else a rich re-soun-ding Ba - ri - tone.

BARITONE SOLO

But the Ba-ri-tone sings of the

glo-rious bat-tle field, He's a sol-dier, or a sai-lor, And his trus-ty sword he'll wield, He

fights for his coun-try, and he ne - ver fears a foe,_____ He'll de -

- fy the ra-ging tem-pest when the stor-my winds do blow

a tempo

Or he'll turn blood thir-sty pi - rate, or a gip - sy or a thief; His ma - ny oc-cu-pa-tions are al-

- most be - yond be - lief And his might is **so** tre-men-dous he can call the world his own It's a

pri-vi-lege to be a migh-ty Ba - ri - tone____

Ah Ten - or and Ba - ri - tone, we are re-

Ah Ten - or and Ba - ri - tone, we are re-

- spec-tive - ly, We can in mer - ry tone sing most ef - fec-tive - ly;

- spec-tive - ly, We can in mer - ry tone sing most ef - fec-tive - ly;

Song or du - - et, Both show our art, Tri - o, Quar -

Song or du - - et, Both show our art,

sweet me-lo-dic Ten-or   Or else a rich re-sound-ing Ba-ri - tone   He may

sweet me-lo-dious Ten-or   Or else a rich re-sound-ing Ba-ri - tone   He may

ei - ther be a Ten - or   a sweet me-lo-dious Ten-or   Or else a rich re-soun-ding Ba - ri

ei - ther be a Ten - or   a sweet me-lo-dious Ten-or   Or else a rich re-soun-ding Ba - ri

- tone.

- tone.

TOM BOWLING

Arranged by ALFRED MOFFAT

by CHARLES DIBDIN

1. Here a sheer bulk, lies poor Tom Bow-ling, The dar-ling of our crew; No more he'll hear the tem-pest how-ling, For death has broach'd him to: His form was of the man-liest beau-ty, His heart was kind and soft,

© Copyright by Bayley and Ferguson Ltd.,
65 Berkeley Street, Glasgow G3 7DX.
Reproduced by permission.

Plate No. 16400

Faith - ful be - low, Tom did his — du - ty, And now he's gone a -

- loft, _____ And now — he's — gone — a - loft. _____

rit.

a tempo

mp 2. Tom nev - er from his
mf 3. Yet shall poor Tom find

a tempo *rit.* *a tempo*

word de - part - ed, His vir - tues were so — rare, _____ His
plea - sant wea - ther, When He who all com - mands, _____ Shall

WATCHMAN! WHAT OF THE NIGHT?

Words ANON.

Music by J. SARJEANT

© Copyright 1905 Boosey and Co.,

Reproduced by permission of Boosey & Hawkes Music Publishers Ltd., 295 Regent Street, London W.1

Plate No. 16400

what of the night, When sor - row and pain are mine, And the plea - sures of life, so

sweet and bright, No long - er a - round me shine?

ten. *cresc.* *dim.* *ten.*

mf Andante

Andante

Andante

That night of __ sor - row thy

soul May sure - ly pre - pare to meet, But a - way shall the clouds of thy

light, no glim-mer-ing star can light, ___ Shall be ___ my sleep-ing

bed, ___ shall be my sleep - ing bed?

That night is

near, and the cheer - less ___ tomb Shall

112

THE WEE COOPER O' FIFE

Arranged by ALFRED MOFFAT

Not too quick *(The time to be regulated in accordance with the humour of the words)*

© Copyright by Bayley and Ferguson Ltd.,
65 Berkeley Street, Glasgow G3 7DX.
Reproduced by permission.

Plate No. 16400

118

Plate No. 16400

WILL -O' - THE - WISP

by J. W. CHERRY

© Copyright J.B. Cramer & Co. Ltd., 99 St.Martin's Lane, London WC2N 4AZ.
All rights reserved,

Plate No. 16400

rall.

I've seen fall, Or fly from me dis - may'd.
vain for help, And dance round them in death.

Allegretto scherzo

Will - o' - the-wisp, they trem - bling cry, Will - o' - the-wisp, tis he ! Will - o' - the-wisp, they

trem - bling cry, Will-o' - the - wisp, 'tis he ! To mark their fright, as

off they fly, Is mer-ry, is mer-ry, is mer - ry sport for

laugh ho! ho! I laugh at their fol - ly and pain, _____ I laugh at their fol-ly, and laugh at their pain, I

laugh _____ at their fol-ly, I laugh at their fol-ly and pain, _____ I laugh ha! ha! I laugh ho! ho! I

laugh at their fol-ly and pain. _____